This book belongs to:

....

For everyone who's had to learn about the party they weren't invited to,
practise conversation topics, and leave group events feeling like they
said the wrong thing without knowing why.

Nyanda Foday

Birmingham's Young Poet Laureate 2016-2018

To my daughter Zaina-Marie, the reason why I illustrate.
I dedicate this book to you.

Joelle Avelino

This paperback edition first published in 2023 by Andersen Press Ltd.
First published in Great Britain in 2022 by Andersen Press Ltd.,
20 Vauxhall Bridge Road, London SW1V 2SA, UK
Vijverlaan 48, 3062 HL Rotterdam, Nederland

1 3 5 7 9 10 8 6 4 2
British Library Cataloguing in Publication Data available.
ISBN 978 1 83913 149 3

BOOKWORMS

Nyanda Foday Joelle Avelino

Andersen Press

We grow up looking for ourselves
On phone screens,
In movie scenes,
In the streets.

Listen for the sound of voices
that ring perfect cadences
over our own.

Not everyone gets to see
themselves when they're young,
We're told we'll find our tribe –

When we join the right club,

Go to the right sixth form,

Get accepted into the right uni,

Try the right passion,

Marry the right person,

Find our found family.

POEtRY

aRt

And we often do –

Eventually.

Doesn't make it any
less lonely.

So we spend nights curled around curled pages of reread books,

Under covers with phone torches,

In corners of playgrounds

Through lunchtimes in libraries
where the silence hides the lack
of people to talk to...

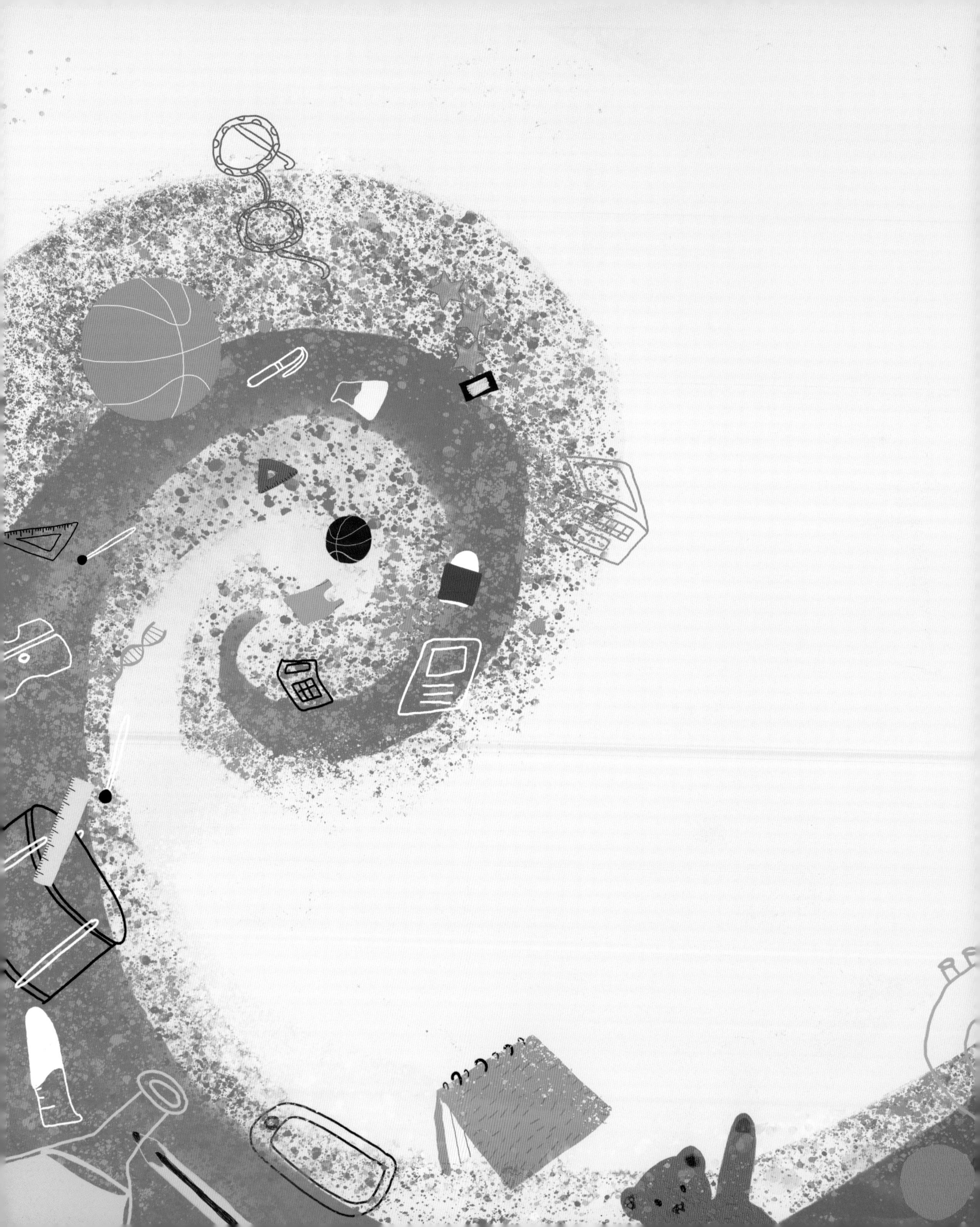

Sometimes a book is the sole piece of driftwood to cling to when it feels like your life is going down with the ship.

And sometimes a character is
enough of a friend to remind you
that there are others like you.

That there is a narrative where
you get to be the protagonist
instead of the scenery.

Sometimes when you're a child,
the only people like you that you can
meet are made of ink and simile,

That's just how it works.

And sometimes the only love you can receive is by proxy.

E
B
a
E
V
K

Society doesn't always teach us what we deserve,
And the only way to learn is through stories
And that anchor is enough to keep us from drifting
out beyond reach.

Because for every break spent between pages there is
another child finishing that same chapter,

And every underrepresented
story is being lived
by someone who
is loved,

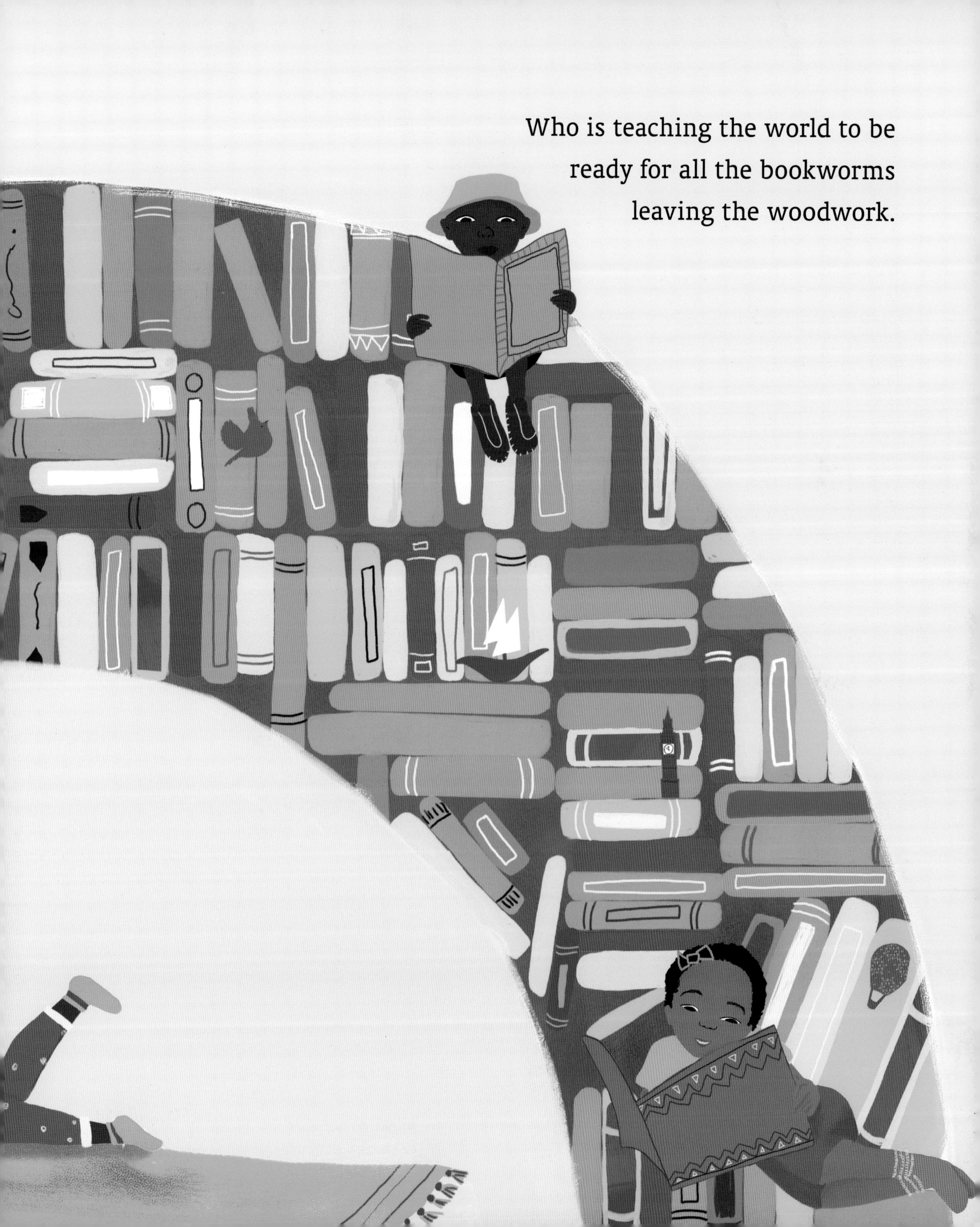

Who is teaching the world to be
ready for all the bookworms
leaving the woodwork.

WE EXIST
OUR StORY MATTERS
WE ARE Worthy
Our TIMe IS HERE
Our voices are Strong

Each publication is a peaceful protest,
A hand outstretched,
A promise that it gets better.

I WILL BE LOVED

That there are families to be found,
And they are so excited to meet each new member.

A good story shows you a new world
The right story shows that you can exist in this one.

Author's Note

Bookworms was a poem born out of a fun series of coincidences and a lifetime of loving books. I wanted to celebrate everything books have done for me, especially through a socially difficult childhood, while still remembering to keep pushing for more. Everyone deserves to see themselves in the stories that they love. The thought that *Bookworms* might serve as a reminder of that for people from all walks of life truly fills me with joy.